AMAZING MAPS
Activity book

Written by Anna Brett

Illustrated by Eilidh Muldoon

ARCTURUS

ARCTURUS

This edition published in 2019 by Arcturus Publishing Limited
26/27 Bickels Yard, 151–153 Bermondsey Street,
London SE1 3HA

ISBN: 978-1-78828-603-9
CH007034NT
Supplier 39, Date 0119, Print run 7079

Illustrations: Eilidh Muldoon
Text: Anna Brett
Design: Amy McSimpson
Editors: Anna Brett and Becca Clunes

Printed in Malaysia

AMAZING MAPS
Activity book

NORTH AMERICA

EUROPE

AFRICA

SOUTH AMERICA

THE WORLD

Our planet is 71 percent covered by water, meaning 29 percent of it is land. The landmasses are divided into seven continents: North America, South America, Europe, Africa, Asia, Australasia and Oceania, and Antarctica. Each continent is then divided up into different countries.

COUNTRIES

Every country is different—they all have their own flag, plus different languages, cultures, animals, habitats, and famous buildings. You can learn about 37 different countries in this book.

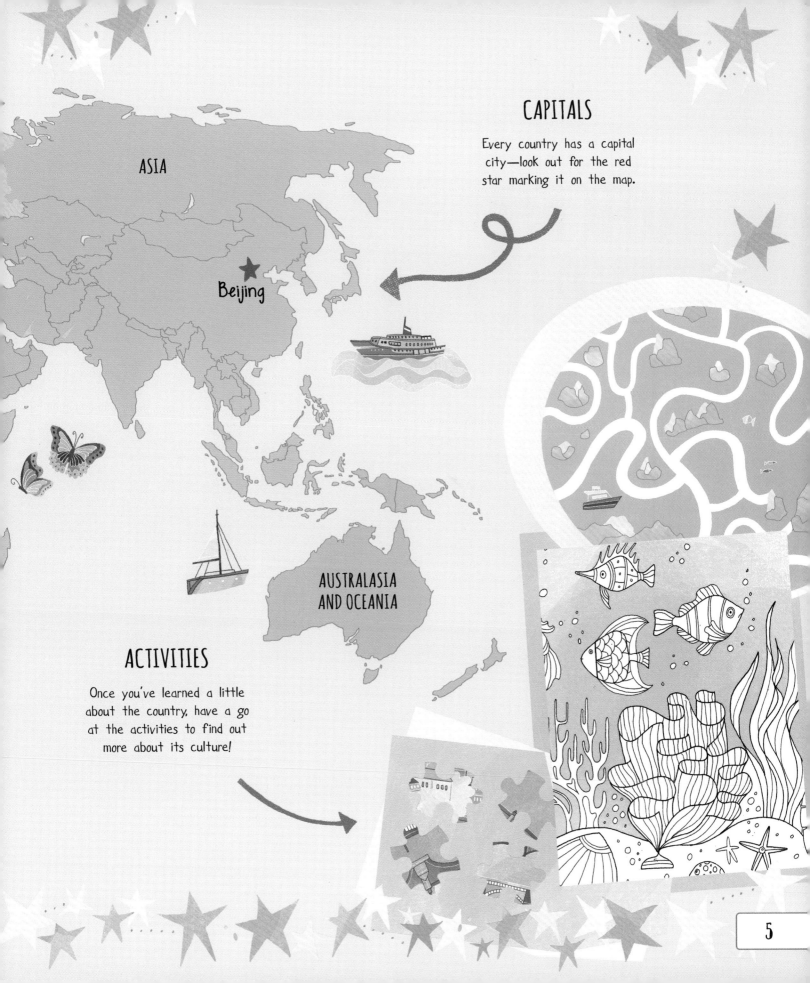

ASIA

Beijing

CAPITALS

Every country has a capital city—look out for the red star marking it on the map.

AUSTRALASIA
AND OCEANIA

ACTIVITIES

Once you've learned a little about the country, have a go at the activities to find out more about its culture!

5

NORTH AMERICA

This continent is in the northern hemisphere and includes Central America and the Caribbean as well as the huge countries of the United States of America (USA) and Canada. Greenland is also in North America, but belongs to the European country of Denmark. North America is surrounded by the Pacific Ocean, the Atlantic Ocean, and the Caribbean Sea.

1

2

3

4

1 CANADA

2 USA

3 MEXICO

4 COSTA RICA

CANADA

Canada is perfect for lovers of the outdoors—it is famous for its high mountains, blue lakes, and large animals, like the moose. It's the second-biggest country in the world, so there's endless exploring to be done.

CANADIAN BEARS

You can find four species of bear in Canada—the polar bear, black bear, grizzly bear, and Kermode bear.

QUEBEC

This area of Canada is mainly French-speaking—English is the other national language.

Hudson Bay

Ottawa

NIAGARA FALLS

This famous natural wonder is actually made up of three different waterfalls: American Falls, Bridal Veil Falls, and Horseshoe Falls.

MOUNTIES

The Royal Canadian Mounted Police wear an iconic red coat and a hat with a wide, flat brim.

TORONTO'S CN TOWER

This was the tallest tower in the world until 2010. You can walk across the glass floor on the observation deck at the top and look down... if you're not afraid of heights!

1 Whistler is popular for skiing.
2 Find moose in the Yukon Territory.
3 Confederation Bridge.
4 Parliament Hill, Ottawa.

Down the Mountain

Can you spot which skier is the odd one out? He's missing an important piece of equipment.

Nature's Playground

Use pens or pencils to finish this beautiful mountainous scene.

USA

The United States of America (USA) is split into 50 different states, some small and others huge. The USA is the birthplace of many famous films, genres of music, and types of sport. This nation also put the first human on the moon!

Alaska

AMERICAN FOOTBALL

This is the most popular spectator sport in America and the annual championship game is called the Super Bowl.

STATUE OF LIBERTY

New York's famous statue is the Roman goddess of freedom and was given to America as a gift from France in 1886.

4

2

1

Washington, D.C.

6

5

3

SPACE RACE

NASA launches many of its rockets into space from the Kennedy Space Center in Florida.

HOLLYWOOD

Many TV series and movies are filmed in glamorous Hollywood, Los Angeles.

Hawaii

HOME OF JAZZ

New Orleans in Louisiana is known as the birthplace of jazz music. The trumpet, saxophone, and double bass are key instruments in a jazz band.

1 Bison are also called buffalo in the USA.
2 Golden Gate Bridge, San Francisco.
3 The White House, Washington, D.C.
4 Mount Rushmore, South Dakota.
5 Empire State Building, New York.
6 Mississippi River.

Spot the Difference

Can you spot five differences between these two jazz bands playing in a club on famous Bourbon Street in New Orleans?

American Icon

Use pencils in browns and creams to finish the animal that became the national emblem of America in 1782.

MEXICO

Ancient ruins, spicy food, and fabulous fiestas make Mexico famous. The country is buzzing with traditions, and there is lots to see and do on the coast, in the forests, and around the cities.

HOT AND SPICY

Mexican food is very tasty, and there is often a spicy kick to the dishes.

CHICHEN ITZA

The ancient Mayan people settled here around 1,000 years ago. The site grew to become one of the largest cities in their empire.

MONARCH BUTTERFLIES

Once a year, millions of monarch butterflies migrate from Canada to Mexico in search of warmer weather. Their wings can span up to 11 cm (4.5 in).

Mexico City

SURF'S UP

Mexico has oceans on both sides of the country, but the Pacific coast is the place for waves. Puerto Escondido is one of the best spots to surf.

1 Cacti grow in the desert regions.

2 Popocatépetl is an active volcano.

3 National Palace, Mexico City.

4 Frida Kahlo painted many self-portraits.

DAY OF THE DEAD

The Day of the Dead is a festival that takes place each year to remember friends and family who have passed away.

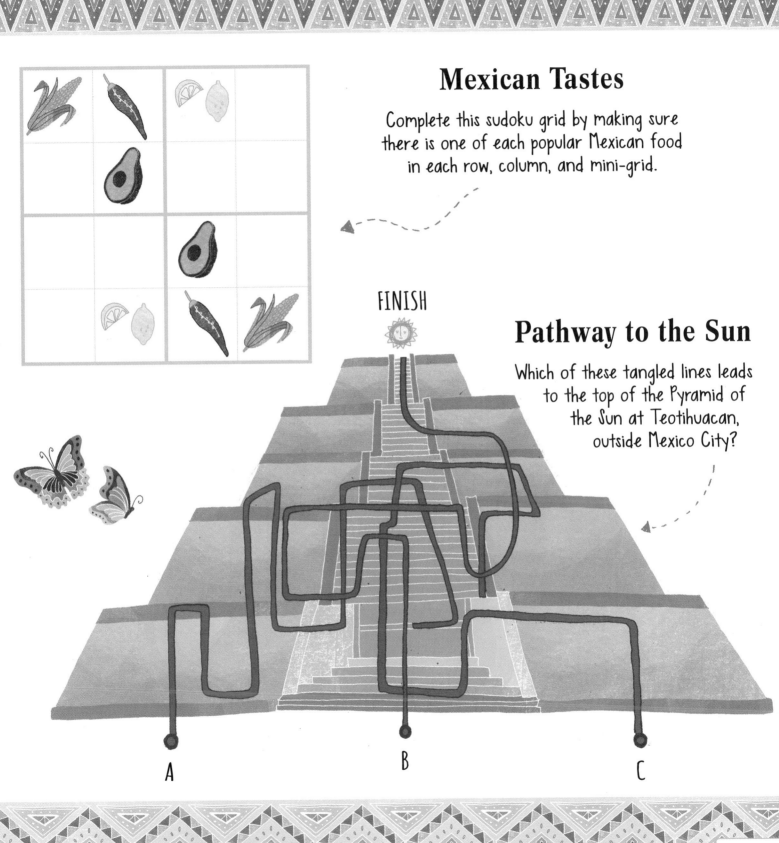

Mexican Tastes

Complete this sudoku grid by making sure there is one of each popular Mexican food in each row, column, and mini-grid.

FINISH

Pathway to the Sun

Which of these tangled lines leads to the top of the Pyramid of the Sun at Teotihuacan, outside Mexico City?

A

B

C

COSTA RICA

This small country in Central America is big on wildlife and wellbeing. The national motto is *pura vida,* meaning "pure life." More than 50 species of hummingbird live a good life in the forests of this beautiful country.

In the Clouds

Cloud forests are so called because their height means they seem to sit in the clouds. You can walk among the treetops on suspension bridges.

Daily Yoga

Stretching out your body and mind has become a hugely popular pastime for Costa Ricans, and tourists.

1 Our Lady of the Angels Basilica, Cartago.

2 La Paz waterfall.

3 Arenal volcano.

San José

Slow Sloths

These cute mammals call Costa Rica home. They may be difficult to spot, though, as their fur is often tinged green to help camouflage them in the trees.

Coffee Growers

Costa Rica grows some of the best coffee beans in the world.

City Culture

The Teatro Nacional in San José opened in 1897 and is beautifully decorated inside.

Ride the Waves

Costa Rica is known for its surfing. Can you spot the five differences between these two sunny surf sessions?

Place the Piece

Which jigsaw piece completes this scene of four hummingbirds in the cloud forest?

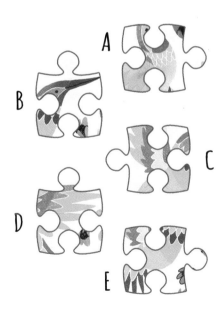

A

B

C

D

E

SOUTH AMERICA

South America is slightly smaller than North America, and is separated from it by the Panama Canal. Habitats include dry deserts, the lush Amazon rain forest, and the longest mountain range in the world—the Andes. The driest place on Earth—the Atacama desert—is also located in South America.

1 COLOMBIA

2 BRAZIL

ORDEM E PROGRESSO

3 PERU

4 ARGENTINA

17

COLOMBIA

Colombia is a country where you can play on a Caribbean beach one day, and trek up snow-covered mountains the next. Mix in some Spanish architecture and fascinating ancient ruins, and this is definitely an exciting place to explore!

LOST CITY

The ancient city of Ciudad Perdida was forgotten about when the Spanish arrived in the 1500s, and only discovered again in the 1970s.

WHITE WATER

Paddle down some white water rapids in San Gil, the adventure capital of the country.

GREEN GEMS

Most of the world's emeralds are mined in Colombia.

★ Bogotá

TEJO SPORT

This national game involves throwing the "tejo" puck at the "bocin" target. Try to avoid hitting the gunpowder-filled "mechas," as they will explode!

CARTAGENA

Many buildings inside this pretty, walled city date back 400 years, to the time when the Spanish ruled here.

1 Andean Condor bird.
2 Go scuba diving in the Caribbean.
3 Plaza Cisneros, Medellín.
4 Monserrate church, Bogotá.

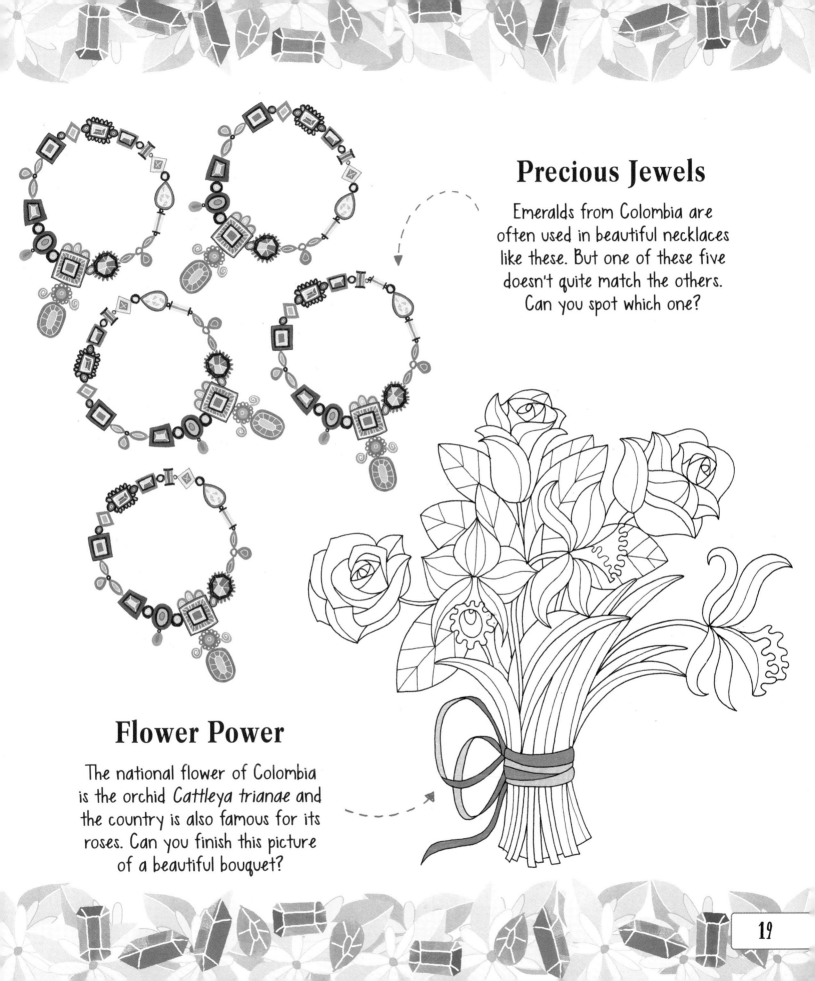

Precious Jewels

Emeralds from Colombia are often used in beautiful necklaces like these. But one of these five doesn't quite match the others. Can you spot which one?

Flower Power

The national flower of Colombia is the orchid *Cattleya trianae* and the country is also famous for its roses. Can you finish this picture of a beautiful bouquet?

BRAZIL

The largest country in South America is famous for its festival of Carnival. Many cities have parades, with music, singing, and dancing. People in the parades often wear costumes inspired by the animals of the Amazon rain forest.

POISON DART FROG

This frog is bright orange as a warning that it is highly toxic!

THE AMAZON RAIN FOREST

This enormous forest is home to at least 40,000 species of plant, 3,000 types of fish, 1,300 different bird species, and 427 varieties of mammal.

CHRIST THE REDEEMER

Rio de Janeiro's most famous sculpture was completed in 1931 and sits high above the city.

1 Amazon Theatre, Manaus.
2 Cathedral Basilica of Salvador.
3 Cathedral of Brasília.
4 Altino Arantes Building, São Paulo.

Brasília

IGUAZÚ FALLS

This is the largest chain of waterfalls in the world and runs across the border with Argentina.

NATIONAL SPORT

The Brazilian national team has won the FIFA World Cup more times than any other country.

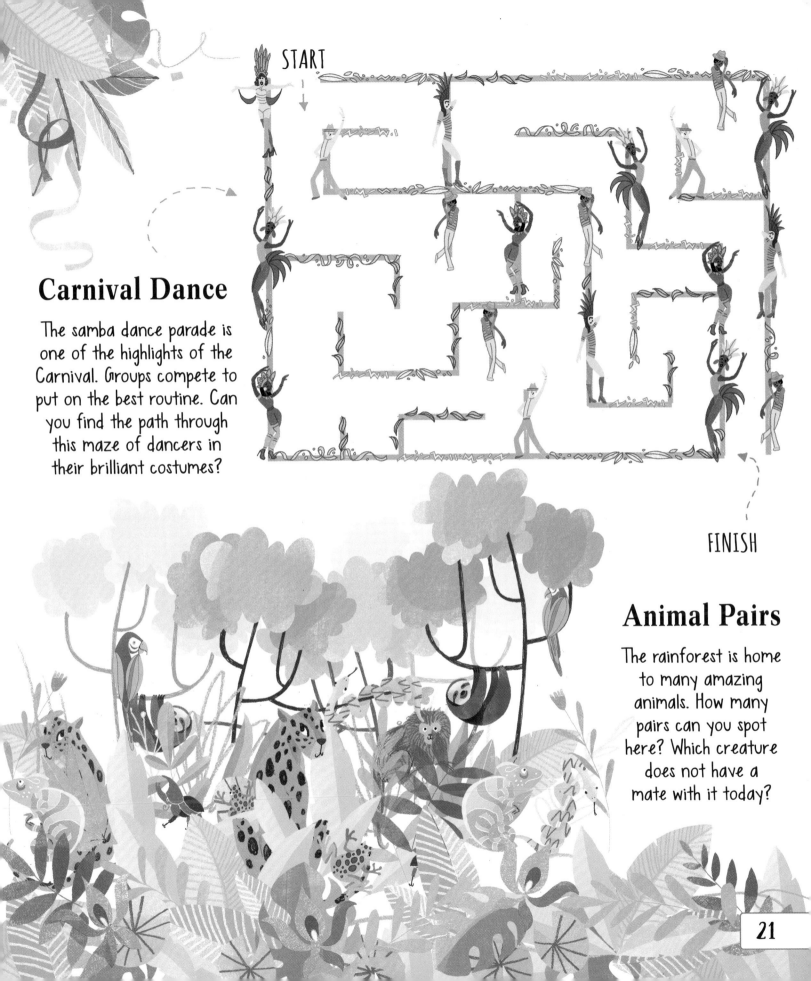

START

Carnival Dance

The samba dance parade is one of the highlights of the Carnival. Groups compete to put on the best routine. Can you find the path through this maze of dancers in their brilliant costumes?

FINISH

Animal Pairs

The rainforest is home to many amazing animals. How many pairs can you spot here? Which creature does not have a mate with it today?

PERU

Fly into Cusco, and you'll arrive in one of the highest-altitude cities in the world. But with a llama-wool sweater to keep you warm, you'll be perfectly positioned to explore the ancient sites of the Incan Empire.

LLAMAS

These mammals are native to Peru and their wool has been used for centuries to make warm clothing and blankets for people living in the mountains.

NAZCA LINES

Lines in the Nazca Desert in southern Peru have been there for around 2,000 years. The lines make geometric shapes and outlines of plants and animals— but no one is quite sure why they were created!

5

Lima

2

3

4

MACHU PICCHU

This ancient city can be found high up on a mountain ridge. It was built for an Incan emperor around 1450, but abandoned 100 years later and forgotten about by the rest of the world until 1911.

CUSCO CATHEDRAL

The building of this Catholic cathedral was begun in 1559 by the Spanish conquistadores. It contains many beautiful pieces of art.

LAKE TITICACA

The largest lake in South America borders Peru and Bolivia. A giant species of frog weighing an enormous 1 kg (2 lb) lives here.

1 Government Palace, Lima.
2 Cathedral Basilica of Lima.
3 The Inca Trail.
4 Andes mountains.
5 Amazon rainforest.

Animal Shapes

Join the dots to reveal one of the animals created by the Nazca lines.

START

14
15 24
13 23 25
12 16
4 5 26
1 6 22
2 3 17 27
7 11
8 10 18 21
9 20 28
19 30 29
31 32 33
44 43 34
45 42 35
57 46 47
58 56
59 55 41 36
60 48
61 54 49 40 37
53 50 39 38
63 62 52 51

FINISH

The Inca Trail

Can you work out which road on the Inca Trail leads to Machu Picchu? The others will take you to more ancient sites that were once populated by the Incan people.

A
B
C

MACHU PICCHU

ARGENTINA

You won't be able to take your eyes off this big, bright nation as it dances its way into your heart. The people here are passionate about sport, food, and their beautiful countryside, so twirl up and celebrate their culture with them.

NATIONAL FLAG MEMORIAL

This complex celebrates the national flag, first raised by creator Manuel Belgrano in 1812.

GAUCHOS

South American Gauchos are cowboys who look after cattle and roam the Pampa fields (grasslands).

PERITO MORENO GLACIER

A glacier is a slow-moving mass of ice. This one in the southern Patagonia region of Argentina is around 30 km (19 miles) long.

Buenos Aires

THE TANGO

The Argentine tango is danced by two people. The moves were created by dancers in Buenos Aires more than 100 years ago.

NATIONAL FLAG MEMORIAL

The pink building in Buenos Aires is the Government House and office of the President of Argentina.

1 A popular drink is a tea called mate.

2 Floralis Genérica sculpture, Buenos Aires.

3 Soccer is the most popular sport.

4 Andes mountain range.

5 Iguazú Falls.

Bold and Bright

La Boca is an area of Buenos Aires famous for its bright buildings and tango dancers performing in the street. Can you work out which jigsaw piece completes this picture of the suburb?

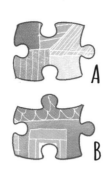

A

B

C

D

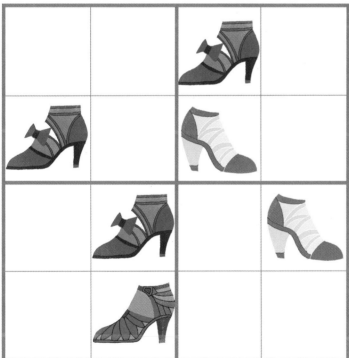

Step by Step

Ladies wear special high heels to dance the tango. Can you make sure each row, column, and mini-grid has one of each shoe? You'll need to draw your own design for the fourth shoe in the puzzle!

EUROPE

Europe is physically connected to Asia, but the Ural Mountains in the east form the boundary between the two continents. Turkey and Russia are countries that span both continents. Europe has one tenth of the world's population, and the world's smallest countries—Vatican City and Monaco.

1 IRELAND

2 UK

3 SWEDEN

4 FINLAND

5 THE NETHERLANDS

6 FRANCE

7 SPAIN

8 PORTUGAL

9 ITALY

10 GERMANY

11 POLAND

12 CZECH REPUBLIC

13 SLOVAKIA

14 GREECE

15 TURKEY

IRELAND

The luck of the Irish is famous! It may be because they believe Saint Patrick, their patron saint, is always watching over them, or it may just be because they are lucky to live on such a naturally beautiful island.

CLIFFS OF MOHER

These sea cliffs rising above the Atlantic Ocean are one of the most visited destinations in Ireland.

BLARNEY STONE

In 1446, a piece of limestone rock was built into the wall of Blarney Castle. Legend says that if you kiss it you'll be given the gift of eloquence.

IRISH MUSIC

Traditional Irish folk music often uses these instruments.

1

Dublin ★

2

IRISH SETTER

This Irish breed of dog is known for its beautiful chestnut coat and friendly manner.

3

SAINT PATRICK'S CATHEDRAL

Founded in 1191, this is the National Cathedral of Ireland. It is named after the patron saint of Ireland, Saint Patrick.

1 Bunratty Castle, Country Clare.

2 Trinity College Dublin, the University of Dublin.

3 Rock of Cashel, County Tipperary.

Stained Glass Saint

The image of Saint Patrick appears in many stained glass windows in churches around Ireland. Can you spot the five differences between these two images of him?

Irish Dancing

Music and dance are popular pastimes in Ireland. Help get these Irish dancers ready for the competition by finishing their beautifully bright, patterned costumes.

UK

The United Kingdom (UK) is made up of England, Scotland, Wales, and Northern Irelandand—and the country's famous royal family is there as a figurehead for it all. Each nation has its own special landmarks that shine a light on the local culture.

1 Find monster Nessie in Loch Ness, Scotland.

2 Canterbury Cathedral, Kent.

3 The Brecon Beacons, Wales.

4 Giant's Causeway, Northern Ireland.

5 The White Cliffs of Dover.

6 Ben Nevis, Scotland.

EDINBURGH CASTLE

Edinburgh is the capital of Scotland and parts of the castle have been there for around 900 years.

ANGEL OF THE NORTH

This steel sculpture by British artist Antony Gormley is 20 m (66 ft) tall and its wings stretch 54 m (177 ft) across.

BUCKINGHAM PALACE

This has been the official London home of the British monarch since 1837. It has 775 rooms!

ROBIN HOOD

This famous English figure lived in Sherwood Forest. He was said to have robbed the rich to give to the poor.

London

STONEHENGE

This prehistoric monument is a ring of huge standing stones over 4,000 years old. It may have been a burial site, but no one knows for sure.

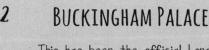

From Land's End to John O'Groats

Can you navigate the way from John O'Groats in the far north of mainland Britain to Land's End in the very south?

Crown Jewels

The Queen has a huge collection of precious jewels, most of which are kept in the Tower of London. But which of these shiny items on display is the odd one out?

START: John O'Groats

FINISH : Land's End

SWEDEN

In the cold north of Europe, Sweden is a country that will warm your heart. It is a member of a group of countries known as Scandinavia. You can view the northern lights here making beautiful patterns in the sky.

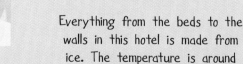

ICE HOTEL

Everything from the beds to the walls in this hotel is made from ice. The temperature is around −5°C (23°F), but you're given a polar-strength sleeping bag to snuggle down into at night!

NORTHERN LIGHTS

This natural light display in the sky can be green, pink, yellow, blue, or violet.

NOBEL MUSEUM

Alfred Nobel founded the Nobel Prize to celebrate the highest achievements in chemistry, literature, peace, physics, economic sciences, and physiology or medicine.

FESKEKÔRKA FISH MARKET

This fish market looks like a church from the outside, but inside it's full of the catch of the day.

Stockholm

ÖRESUND BRIDGE

This bridge crosses the water between Sweden and Denmark. It takes about 10 minutes to drive across.

1 Reindeer live in the north.

2 The Picasso Sculpture, Kristinehamn.

3 Turning Torso skyscraper, Malmö.

4 Kiruna church, Kiruna.

Scandi Friends

The Scandinavian countries of Iceland, Norway, Sweden, Finland, and Denmark have shared cultures. Can you pair up these Scandi icons and then find the one that doesn't belong to this culture?

Dog Sled Team

Join the dots to complete this picture of a musher with his husky dogs.

START

FINLAND

Welcome to the land of the midnight sun. Finland is so far north that in the summer months that the sun never quite sets behind the horizon, meaning 24 hours of light. The Finns embrace these long days before the snowy winter returns.

MOOMINWORLD

Finnish artist Tove Jansson created the Moomin characters and her stories about them are loved by people around the world. Visit the Moomin World theme park to experience life in Moominvalley.

LAPLAND

In winter, the north of the country is a dark, snowy place. But Lapland is a winter wonderland, so no wonder this is said to be the area that Santa calls home.

3

SAUNA SESSIONS

Taking time to relax in a sauna is part of the Finnish culture. High temperatures and the smell of fresh birch leaves help relax the body and mind.

Helsinki

2

1

MIDSUMMER CELEBRATIONS

The last Saturday in June is a national holiday in Finland. People celebrate the arrival of summer and the "white nights" of constant daylight.

THE SAMI PEOPLE

The Sami are the indigenous people of northern Europe and reindeer herding is a traditional part of their culture.

1 Helsinki Cathedral.

2 The Rock Church, Helsinki.

3 Around 1,500 brown bears live in Finland.

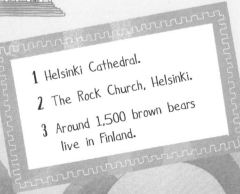

Santa's Workshop

Santa is busy at home in Lapland preparing all the presents he's going to deliver on Christmas Eve. Can you spot five differences between these two pictures of him with his helpers?

Pretty Patterns

Can you complete this traditional Sami outfit by coping the pattern from the right side of the "gakti" tunic onto the left?

THE NETHERLANDS

More than 25 percent of the Netherlands is below sea level, and another 50 percent of it is less than 1m (3 ft) above sea level. Amsterdam, the capital city, is so low-lying that all the houses are built on hidden stilts!

AMSTERDAM

The capital city is crisscrossed by canals, and so there are more than 1,200 bridges to enable people to cross them!

WHIRLING WINDMILLS

The country is so flat that farmland is prone to flooding. Windmills can help pump excess water off the land and into the rivers.

THE HAGUE

This city is home to the Dutch parliament and also the United Nation's International Court of Justice.

Amsterdam

PRETTY TULIPS

The country blooms into a sea of flowers in spring. Tulips grow so well here they are exported around the world.

ANNE FRANK

Anne and her Jewish family had to go into hiding in this house in Amsterdam to escape the Nazis during World War II. You can read the diary she kept while living here.

1 Amsterdamse Poort, Haarlem.

2 Dom Tower, Utrecht.

3 Royal Palace of Amsterdam.

4 Cycling is a popular mode of transport.

Flower Field

Can you fill in this field of flowers so that there is one type of bloom in each row, column, and mini-grid?

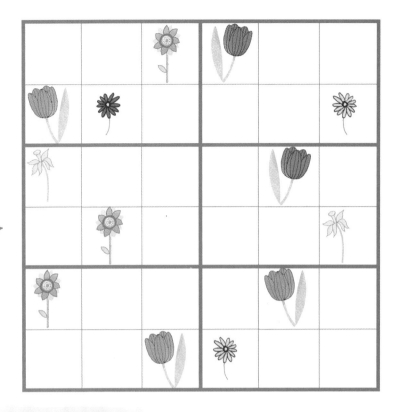

Which Water Way?

Can you find your way from start to finish, going past all three bicycles? You're not allowed to retrace your path.

FINISH

START

FRANCE

France is as pretty as a picture and as exciting as an action movie! There's so much to see in Paris, the capital, that millions of people visit each year. When you need a break from sightseeing, settle down to a delicious French meal.

1 Palace of Versaille.

2 Notre-Dame Cathedral, Paris.

3 Chamonix is a good place to ski.

THE LOUVRE

This art gallery and museum is the biggest in the world, showcasing 38,000 pieces. It has a glass pyramid at the entrance.

MONT SAINT-MICHEL

This island off the coast is home to an abbey. At low tide it's possible to walk over from the mainland, but luckily a causeway was built for when the high tide blocks the way back.

Paris

2

1

3

EIFFEL TOWER

Almost 7 million people visit France's famous monument every year. There are 1,710 steps in total, but visitors can only climb up to the first platform (330 steps, or just take the elevator!).

FOOD AND DRINK

France is famous for its cuisine—cheese, croissants, and champagne are some of its famous delicacies.

FILM FESTIVAL

The town of Cannes hosts an international film festival every year and prizes are awarded to the best new films.

Don't Let the Tower Topple!

Which of these jigsaw pieces do you need to complete Paris's famous tower?

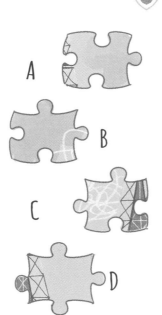

Famous Lady

The *Mona Lisa* by Leonardo da Vinci is displayed in the Louvre and is one of the most famous paintings in the world. But there seem to be five mistakes in this copy of the painting on the right. Can you spot them all?

SPAIN

When thinking of Spain, its sunny beaches and fun fiestas might be the first things that spring to mind. But it's also a country with amazing architecture and a long history, so there's lots to discover.

GUGGENHEIM MUSEUM

Designed by Frank Gehry, this art gallery looks like a huge ship. Many people think of it as one of the best buildings of the twentieth century.

FLAMENCO DANCE

This dance originated in Spain and involves hand-clapping to help keep the tempo of the steps and the music.

Madrid

LA SAGRADA FAMÍLIA

This huge gothic church in Barcelona was designed by Antoni Gaudí and although construction began in 1882, it's still not finished!

PLAZA MAYOR

Madrid's main square was first created in 1619 and is home to a statue of King Phillip III.

ALHAMBRA PALACE

The name for this Islamic palace in Granada comes from the Arabic for "The Red One."

1 Park Güell, Barcelona.

2 Royal Palace of Madrid.

3 Running of the Bulls in Pamplona.

4 Mosque–Cathedral of Córdoba.

5 The Pyrenees.

6 The Costa del Sol.

The Running of the Bulls

The town of Pamplona celebrates the festival of San Fermín every July. One of the events involves people running in front of a group of bulls that have been let loose in a circuit of narrow streets! Can you spot which one of these charging bulls is not quite like the others?

Gaudí's Park

Gaudí also designed Barcelona's Park Güell, which is famous for all the mosaic tiles on the sculptures. Grab your pencils and create your own mosaic patterns on this picture of the park.

PORTUGAL

Portugal is full of treats—sweet ones to eat, natural ones to marvel at, and pretty sights for your eyes to enjoy. Discover ancient towns inland, and beautiful beaches all along the coastline.

BOM JESUS DO MONTE

Climb up the staircase to reach the church at the top of this religious site in northern Portugal.

TASTY TARTS

The iconic sweet Portuguese custard tart was created in 1837 by a bakery in Belém, Lisbon.

LISBON'S TRAMS

Catch a tram to ride around the city. Line 28 is the most iconic, as the historic yellow tram rattles along narrow streets and up steep hills.

3

Lisbon ★

PENA PALACE

This castle on a hill in Sintra is a World Heritage Site. It was built to be a summer house for the royal family.

2

1

CAVE OF BENAGIL

You have to take a boat to reach this spectacular cave on the Algarve coast. The opening in the roof of the cave is called "the eye."

4

1 University of Coimbra.

2 Chapel of Bones, Évora.

3 Tower of Belém, Lisbon.

4 Golf is a popular sport in the Algarve.

Tile Art

Lisbon is famous for all the pretty tiles on walls around the city. Can you complete this grid of tiles by making sure there is one of each pattern in every row, column, and mini-grid?

Take the Tram Across Town

Trace the route the blue tram should take to get to the other side of Lisbon's city. Can you pass four red trams on your way?

START

FINISH

ITALY

If you've ever eaten pizza, pasta, or ice cream, you've had a taste of Italy. But to visit this country is even more delicious, as the ancient cities are famous for their history and the countryside offers endless views of rolling hills or breathtaking beaches.

GONDOLAS TO GO

Venice is a city built on water. To get around you have to travel by boat, and there's no better way to navigate the watery streets than by gondola.

VATICAN CITY

This independent state within Rome is the smallest country in the world and is ruled by the Pope—the head of the Catholic Church.

HORSE RACE

Siena hosts a horse race called the Palio around its ancient Piazza del Campo twice a year.

Rome

THE COLOSSEUM

You can't miss this huge ancient building in the middle of Rome. Roman gladiators fought each other here for the entertainment of others.

LOST CITY

In 79 AD, poor Pompeii and its population was destroyed when Mount Vesuvius erupted and buried everything in volcanic ash.

1 Pizza was invented in Naples.

2 The Leaning Tower of Pisa.

3 Milan is home to designer fashion.

4 Sicily.

5 Sardinia.

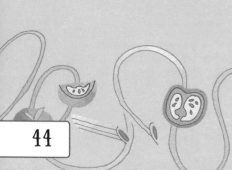

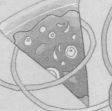

Italian Feast

Can you pair up all these plates of delicious Italian food and drink and discover which one doesn't have a match?

Row Your Boat

Trace the routes to see which gondola has made it to St. Mark's Square to see its famous Basilica?

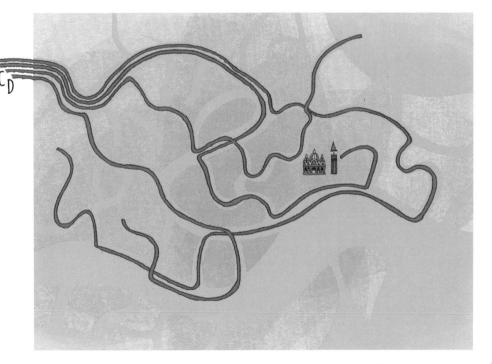

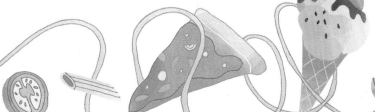

GERMANY

Shine a spotlight on Germany, and you'll discover a country that has inspired fairy tales and classical music. Germany has lots of fantastic places to enjoy art and culture.

FAIRYTALE CASTLE

Ludwig II, King of Bavaria, had Neuschwanstein Castle built to be his home, but he died before it was completed and it's been open to the public ever since.

BRANDENBURG GATE

Berlin's city gate is a symbol of freedom for modern Germany.

1

Berlin ★

OKTOBERFEST

The first of these festivals (which start in September and finish in October) was held in Munich in 1810. People dress in traditional clothes to celebrate—dirndls for women and lederhosen for men.

BLACK FOREST

This forest region in the southwest of the country is associated with the Grimm brothers' fairy tales.

3

2

LUDWIG VAN BEETHOVEN

Born in Germany, Beethoven is one of the world's most famous composers. He wrote many of his best pieces when he became deaf in later life.

1 Berlin is famous for its street art.

2 Every year, Nüremberg holds a Christmas Market.

3 The Reichstag, Berlin, where the parliament meets.

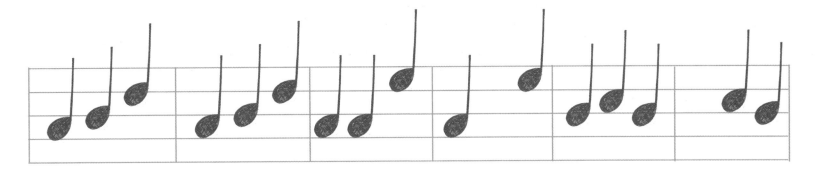

Musical Notes

Look at the sequence of these musical notes and see if you can draw in the two missing notes to complete the tune.

Sleeping Beauty

Neuschwanstein Castle was said to be the inspiration for the castle in Disney's Sleeping Beauty. Can you spot the five differences between the real castle and the fairytale one?

POLAND

Poland's ancient history is full of mythical tales and stargazing into space. It is a country with strong traditions and lots of castles and countryside to explore.

GDANSK

This city sits on the coast and its medieval port is very pretty.

1

NICOLAUS COPERNICUS

This Polish astrologer became famous for realizing that the Sun was at the middle of our solar system, not the Earth. There's a monument to him in Warsaw.

AUSCHWITZ

The Nazis built a concentration camp at Auschwitz during World War II. More than a million people were killed here, and the museum helps us to remember them.

2

Warsaw

SUPER SALT MINE

The Wieliczka salt mine produced table salt until 2007 and is now an underground attraction boasting chapels, statues, and carvings all made out of salt.

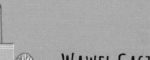

WAWEL CASTLE

In the historic area of Kraków, this castle was once home to the Kings of Poland and is now an art gallery.

1 Museum of World War II, Gdansk.
2 Bison live in the Białowieża National Park.

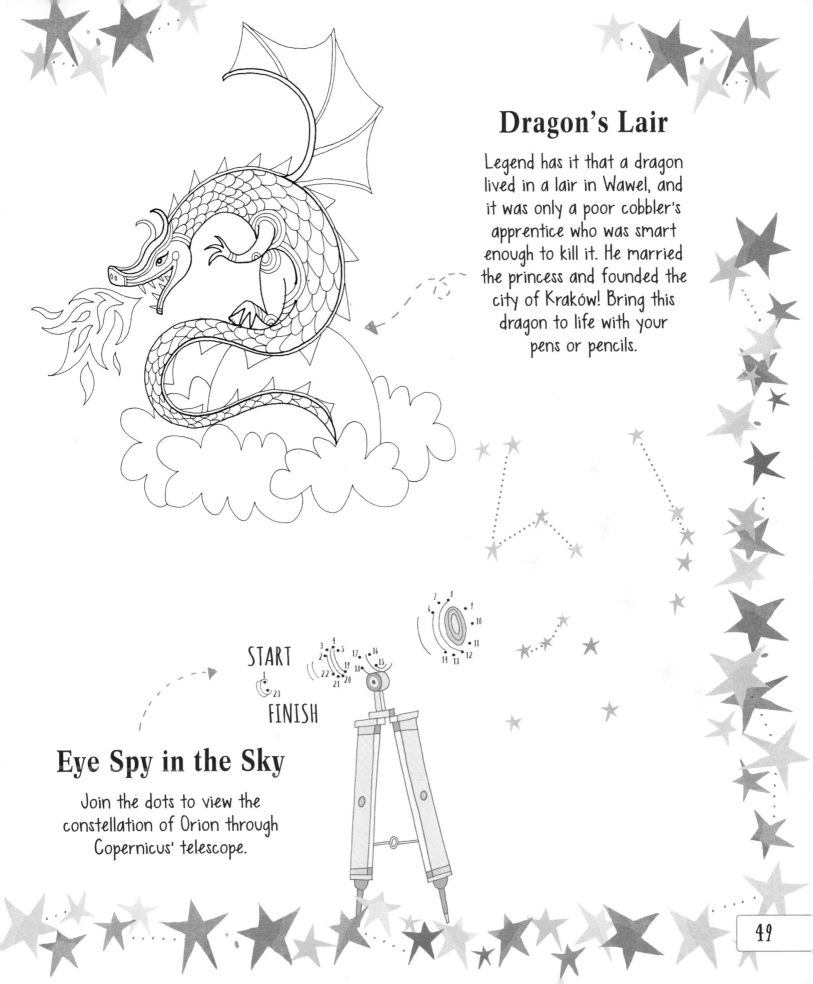

Dragon's Lair

Legend has it that a dragon lived in a lair in Wawel, and it was only a poor cobbler's apprentice who was smart enough to kill it. He married the princess and founded the city of Kraków! Bring this dragon to life with your pens or pencils.

Eye Spy in the Sky

Join the dots to view the constellation of Orion through Copernicus' telescope.

START

FINISH

CZECH REPUBLIC

The Czech Republic is known for its castles and Prague's most famous medieval bridge. But outside of the city it is all about music, dance, and arts as traditional folklore is celebrated.

1 Find the Singing Fountain in the Royal Gardens, Prague Castle.

2 Strahov Library, Prague.

3 Museum of Glass, Karlovy Vary.

4 Television Tower, Prague.

BOHEMIAN PARADISE

The sandstone rock formations in this UNESCO forest area have names like Dragon's Tooth, Lighthouse, and Choirmaster.

LEGO MUSEUM

Visit the largest Lego museum in Europe—there are over 2,000 models on display!

Prague

CHARLES BRIDGE

This historic bridge crosses the river Vltava in Prague and was the only route across the water until 1841. It's named after King Charles IV, a Holy Roman Emperor.

PRAGUE CASTLE

This magnificent building is the largest castle complex in the world. Parts of it date back to the ninth century and it's now the office of the President of the Czech Republic.

CHODSKO FOLK FESTIVAL

This festival celebrates the traditional culture of the region. People have been enjoying bagpipe music, folk dancing, and a traditional fair here every year since 1955.

Dressed to Dance

These dancers are performing a traditional routine, but one of them doesn't quite have a complete outfit. Can you spot what they are missing?

Prague Puzzle

There are 17 bridges in Prague, but one of them is missing a piece in this jigsaw puzzle picture. Which one completes the scene?

A

B

C

D

SLOVAKIA

Slovakia may be landlocked, but there's plenty of water to find as it rushes down mountains in falls, flows gently along the Danube river, and pools in picturesque lakes made by glaciers. There are plenty of natural spa sites to discover too.

TATRA MOUNTAIN

Hop on a mountain bike to explore the trails in summer and then clip into skis to see the area in the snowy winter months.

NATIONAL PARK

Hike around the Slovenský Raj national park and discover waterfalls thundering over cliff edges.

ST. MARTIN'S CATHEDRAL

You can't miss this Cathedral in the Old Town of Bratislava, it's been here for more than 500 years.

SPIŠ CASTLE

This castle is huge—it's one of the largest in central Europe. Climb to the top of the tower for views of the area.

Bratislava

BOAT ACROSS THE BORDER

Fancy a day trip to another country? It takes just 75 minutes by boat to travel from Bratislava to Vienna in Austria.

1 Trenčin Castle.

2 Chmarošský Viaduct.

3 Monument in Banská Štiavnica.

FINISH

A B C

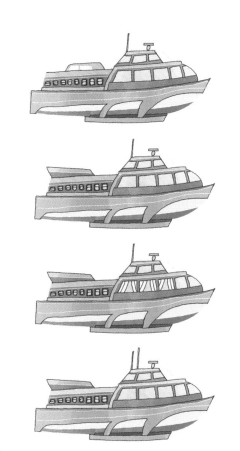

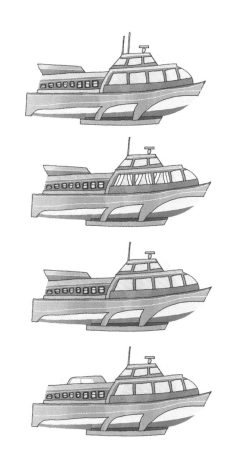

Hydrofoil Pairs

These boats on skis whizz passengers into Bratislava from Austria. Each boat has a pair, can you match them up?

Top of the Tower

Built in around 1300, Michael's Gate is one of the oldest buildings in Bratislava and used to be one of only four entrances into the city. Which route takes you to the balcony at the top?

GREECE

The Ancient Greeks gave so much to the world—including hosting the first Olympics! With around 6,000 islands to explore, a boat is the best way to see lots of the country.

METEORA ROCKS

Monasteries sit on top of huge towers of smooth rock to create a site that's special to the religious and natural world.

SANTORINI

The island of Santorini was created when a volcano collapsed into the sea. It's high cliffs are dotted with iconic white buildings with blue roofs.

ACROPOLIS

On top of a hill above the city of Athens sits an ancient group of buildings, the most famous is the Parthenon—dedicated to the goddess Athena.

1

Athens

2

DELPHI

Delphi was a very important, sacred place to the Ancient Greeks. A wise person called the Oracle lived here in central Greece and had wisdom passed down to her from the god Apollo.

SAIL AWAY

Only 227 of the 6,000 Greek islands are inhabited, but that's still plenty to explore on a sailboat!

1 The Parthenon, Athens.
2 Olympia is the site of the ancient Olympic Games.

Water Ways

Can you sail from Athens to Rhodes, the island farthest away from the Greek capital?

START

FINISH

Greek God

King of the Greek gods, Zeus is a sky god who controls the thunder and lightning. Join the dots to complete this picture of him.

TURKEY

East meets west in this country as it sits on the continents of Europe and Asia. You can see why ancient civilizations built their cities here—parts of the landscape are out of this world.

HAGIA SOPHIA

This building in Istanbul with the famous dome has been a Greek Orthodox church, a Roman Catholic cathedral, and an Ottoman mosque, and is now a museum.

HOT AIR BALLOONS

The rocky landscape of Cappadocia is best viewed from above, so take to the skies in a hot air balloon and look down on the stone columns below you.

WEST TO EAST

Take the ferry from Europe to Asia by cruising along the Bosporus strait in Istanbul.

Istanbul

3

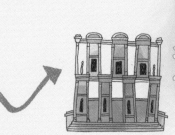

EPHESUS RUINS

These ruins were once an ancient Greek city but are now part of Turkey. The famous Temple of Artemis on the site is one of the Seven Wonders of the Ancient World.

2

1

PAMUKKALE POOLS

These bright white terraces are covered in brilliant blue water. The name means "Cotton Castle" in Turkish.

1 Bazaars, Istanbul.

2 Bodrum Beach.

3 The Blue Mosque.

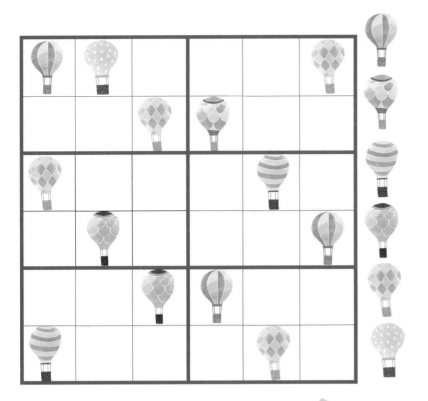

High in the Sky

These hot air balloons are making a pattern in the sky—there needs to be one of each design in every row, column, and mini-grid. Can you instruct them where to fly to complete the pattern?

Islamic Pattern Art

The domes in the Blue Mosque are decorated in beautiful repeating patterns. Can you fill in the two missing blocks to complete this design?

AFRICA

This is the second-largest continent in terms of landmass and population. The equator runs through the middle of Africa and habitats include hot deserts (the Sahara is the world's largest hot desert), jungles, and the savanna grasslands. The largest city in Africa is Lagos, in Nigeria.

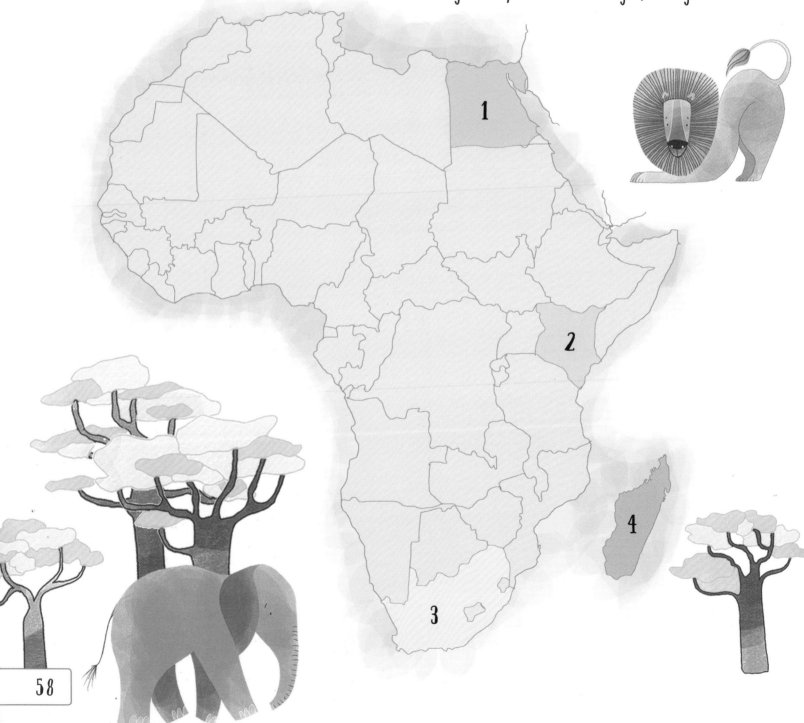

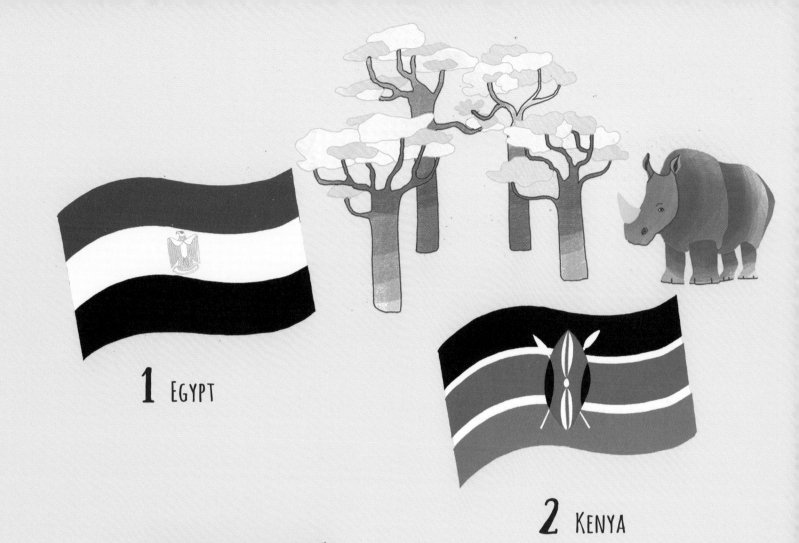

1 EGYPT

2 KENYA

3 SOUTH AFRICA

4 MADAGASCAR

EGYPT

The jewels in Egypt's crown were created by its ancient civilization thousands of years ago. Many of the key sites sit along the river Nile—it cuts through the country and nourishes the dry desert land around it.

THE RED SEA

This inlet of water from the Indian Ocean is home to tropical fish and is the perfect place to snorkel.

1 The Suez Canal.

2 The Mosque of Muhammad Ali.

3 The River Nile.

GREAT GIZA

The pyramids at Giza have been standing for around 4,500 years and were built as tombs for the pharaohs who ruled Egypt. The Sphinx next to them may have been built for the Pharaoh Khafre.

EGYPTIAN MUSEUM

Discover the treasures of ancient Egypt at this museum—the highlight is Tutankhamun's gold burial mask.

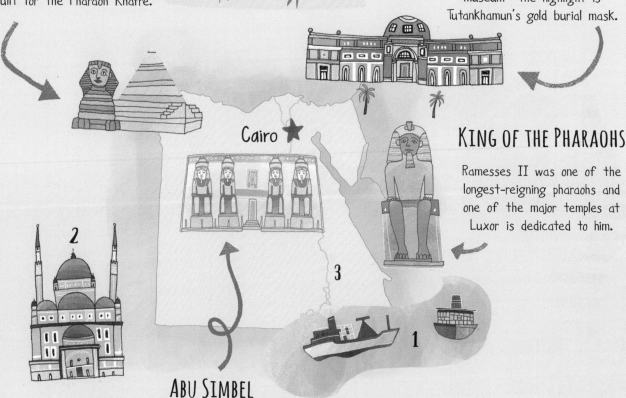

Cairo

KING OF THE PHARAOHS

Ramesses II was one of the longest-reigning pharaohs and one of the major temples at Luxor is dedicated to him.

ABU SIMBEL

Four huge statues sit at the entrance to this temple in the south of the country ... all of them are of Ramesses II!

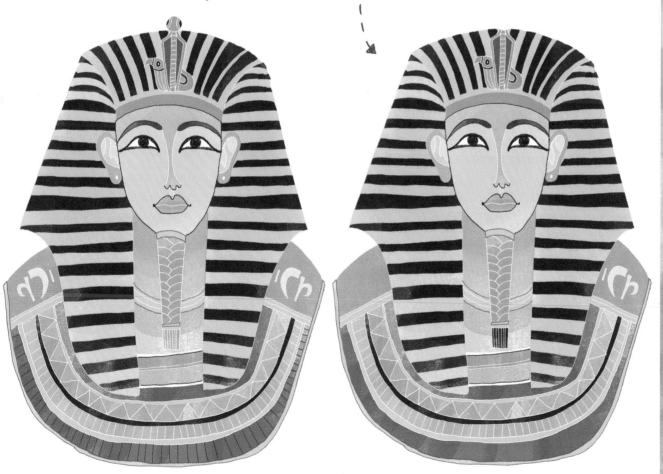

Missing Symbols

The Ancient Egyptians wrote using hieroglyphics and the symbols often look like the words they represent. Can you spot each sequence used here and fill in the missing icons?

Two Tutankhamuns?

This golden, jewel-encrusted mask was found in Tutankhmun's tomb and is one of the most famous pieces of art in the world. Can you spot the five differences between the real mask and the fake copy?

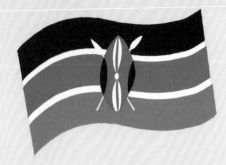

KENYA

Go on safari across the savanna to see all the amazing animals that call this country home. Groups of people, such as the Maasai, share the land with these beasts and will also give you a warm welcome.

THE BIG FIVE

Visit the national parks and you're in with a chance of seeing the famous "big five" animals—lions, leopards, rhinos, African elephants, and African buffalos.

1

THE MAASAI PEOPLE

This group of people live a semi-nomadic lifestyle, following their livestock around the land. They are known for their group dance that involves jumping high into the air.

★ Nairobi

3

WILDEBEEST MIGRATION

2

Every year, herds containing more than 1.5 million wildebeest move across the savanna in search of food.

KEEP ON RUNNING

Many of the world's best long-distance runners are Kenyan.

PINK FLAMINGOS

Huge numbers of pink flamingos live on the shore of Lake Nakuru. It's their diet of shrimp and algae that turns their feathers pink!

1 Mount Kenya.

2 Lake Turkana.

3 Nairobi is the biggest city in east Africa.

Spot the Spots

Can you pair up the leopards according to their spots?

Sea of Pink

How many flamingo feet are in the water?

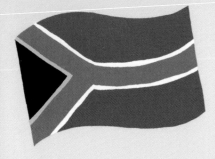

SOUTH AFRICA

The most southerly country in Africa has lots to offer the outdoor explorer—a beautiful coastline, national reserves, and many mountains to hike up. It has warm sunny summers, even though the next stop on a journey south is Antarctica!

BUNGEE JUMPING

In the adventure capital of Africa, experience the highest bridge bungee jump in the world at Bloukrans Bridge.

4

SHINE BRIGHT

The diamond mine in Kimberley is the largest in the world and this "Big Hole" can be seen from space.

1

★ Pretoria

TABLE MOUNTAIN

Climb up to the top of this mountain for amazing views of Cape Town and gaze south to see the edge of the continent.

PENGUINS ON THE BEACH

You may think penguins only live in Antarctica, but head to Boulders Beach to visit these tropical cousins.

NATIONAL PARK

3

2

NELSON MANDELA

Nelson Mandela united the country in the 1990s after much political and social unrest, and was South Africa's first black president.

1 Hillbrow Tower, Johannesburg.

2 Ostriches are farmed throughout the country.

3 Kruger National Park.

4 The Lighthouse, Cape Point.

FINISH

START

Table Top

Take care and try to follow the correct path to reach the top of Table Mountain.

Beach Bathers

The colony of African penguins living on Boulders Beach settled there in 1982. Which jigsaw piece should you use to complete the scene?

MADAGASCAR

This island is home to incredible species of plant and animal that can't be found anywhere else in the world. Explore the rainforest, desert, canyons, and mountains to find them and enjoy this one-of-a-kind country.

THE KNIFE FOREST

The Tsingy de Bemaraha National Park is full of razor-sharp spikes of limestone rock.

LOADS OF LEMURS

The most iconic of all Madagascar's animals is the lemur. The ringtail has a black-and-white-striped tail.

BAOBAB TREES

These native trees have huge trunks and can live for over a thousand years.

BROOKESIA CHAMELEON

These tiny chameleons are some of the smallest reptiles around. The *Brookesia micra* is only 30 mm (1¼ in) long.

Antananarivo

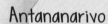

3

ROYAL HILL OF AMBOHIMANGA

Perched on top of a hill, this sacred site is home to a traditional royal settlement that was once the capital of the country.

2

1 Humpback whales visit the coastal waters.

2 There are rock formations in the Isalo National Park.

3 There is a Blue Pool in the Isalo National Park.

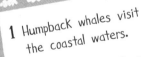

1

Link up the Lemur

Madame Berthe's mouse lemur is the smallest primate in the world. Join the dots to finish drawing this one.

START

FINISH

Changing Chameleon

Chameleons are usually green to camouflage themselves in the trees, but they signal to each other by turning red, blue, yellow, pink, and orange. How will you decorate this chameleon?

ASIA

Asia is the largest continent by landmass and population. Around 60 percent of the world's population live in Asia with the two most populated countries being China and India. This continent contains Arctic northern lands and tropical southern islands. It also has the world's highest mountains.

1 UAE

2 RUSSIA

3 INDIA

4 NEPAL

5 CHINA

6 SOUTH KOREA

7 JAPAN

8 VIETNAM

UAE

The United Arab Emirates is made up of seven emirate states: Abu Dhabi, Ajman, Fujairah, Sharjah, Dubai, Ras Al Khaimah, and Umm Al Quwain. It was formed in 1971 and has grown quickly—just look up to see hundreds of huge skyscrapers.

BURJ KHALIFA

The tallest building in the world is in Dubai. It measures an incredible 830 m (2,722 ft).

1 The Emirates Palace, Abu Dhabi.

2 The Yas Marina Circuit.

3 Louvre Abu Dhabi has artworks from museums across France.

2

3

Abu Dhabi

1

TRADITIONAL SOUKS

Beyond the modern buildings, traditional markets called souks are still alive in Dubai. The Gold Souk glitters with all its goods.

LAND OF SAND

The UAE is located in the Arabian desert, so outside of the cities there's sand as far as the eye can see.

GRAND MOSQUE

The Sheikh Zayed Grand Mosque in Abu Dhabi is the largest in the country and there's space for more than 40,000 people.

FALCON FRIENDS

Falcons are the national bird of the UAE and a popular pet. If they get sick, they can go to the Abu Dhabi Falcon Hospital, the first of its kind.

To the Top

It takes one minute to travel to the top of the Burj Khalifa in the elevator. How quickly can you work out which line makes it to the top in this puzzle?

FINISH

A B C D

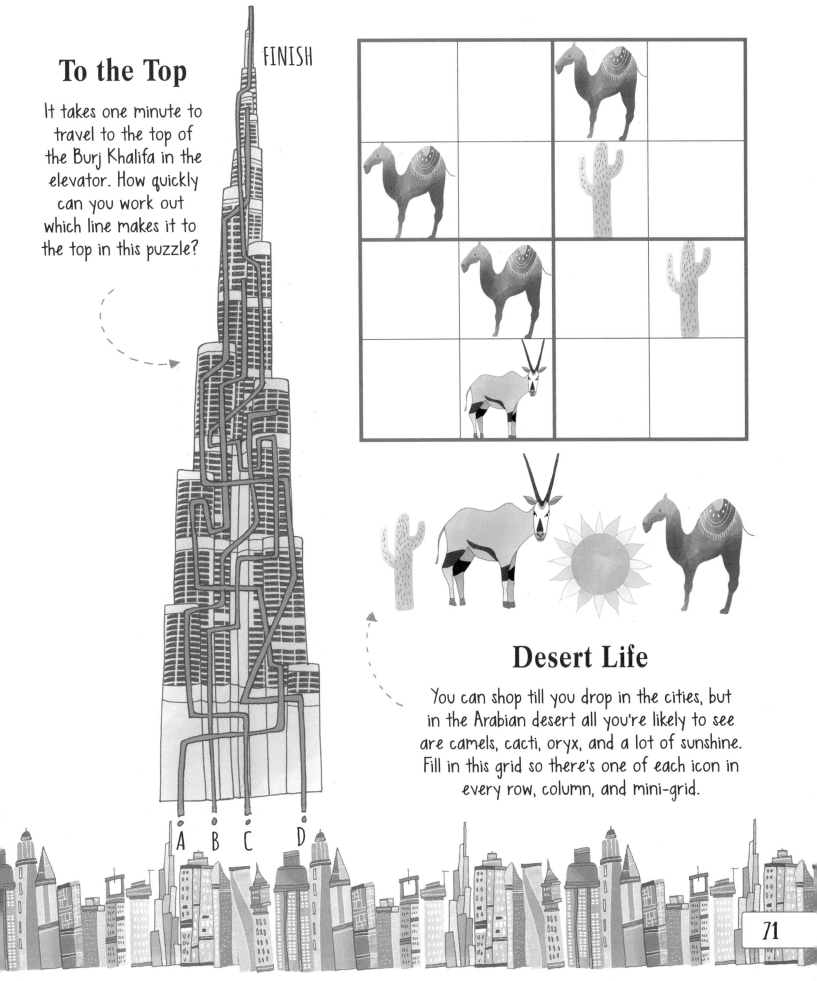

Desert Life

You can shop till you drop in the cities, but in the Arabian desert all you're likely to see are camels, cacti, oryx, and a lot of sunshine. Fill in this grid so there's one of each icon in every row, column, and mini-grid.

RUSSIA

The largest country in the world crosses nine time zones, so it's no surprise that it's home to the world's longest railroad! The forested area of Siberia covers 75 percent of Russia, so head to the big cities to discover the history of the country.

LAKE BAIKAL

This is the largest freshwater lake in the world. It is also the deepest at 1,640 m (5,380 ft).

1

2

3

Moscow

THE KREMLIN

At the heart of Moscow, this citadel includes five palaces and four cathedrals and is now home to the President.

TRANS-SIBERIAN RAILROAD

The world's longest railroad line connects Moscow with the far east of the country.

FABERGÉ MUSEUM

Fabergé Eggs are elaborate pieces of art containing a surprise inside. Imperial Easter Fabergé Eggs were commissioned by the Russian Royal Family and only 50 were made, so they are extremely valuable.

1 The Mariinsky Theatre of Opera and Ballet, St. Petersburg.

2 The State Hermitage Museum, St. Petersburg.

3 Siberian wolves live in the far north.

ST. BASIL'S CATHEDRAL

This cathedral, located in the Red Square in Moscow, was built by Ivan the Terrible. There are nine separate chapels around the central nave.

Odd Egg Out

Fabergé Eggs are covered in jewels and worth millions. But can you spot the fake in this line-up?

Sweet Treats

The towers on St. Basil's Cathedral look like ice creams! Which types of sweet treat will you decorate the building with?

INDIA

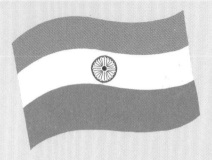

Sacred sites and scents of spice in the air sum up this vibrant country. It's no surprise that the country is rich with history, architecture, festivals, and culture, as more than a billion people call India home.

INDIAN CUISINE

India is famous for its curries. The aroma from the mix of spices that go into them floats in the air, ready to tickle your taste buds.

1

New Delhi

THE GANGES

The longest river in the country is a sacred site for Hindus and many pilgrims travel here to bathe in the water.

2

4

TAJ MAHAL

Built as a tribute to Emperor Shah Jahan's wife, this is one of the most romantic buildings in the world... and one of the most photographed, due to its symmetry!

3

HOLI FESTIVAL

This festival marks the start of Spring and those involved in the celebrations throw bright red, blue, yellow, and green powders over each other.

BENGAL TIGER

This species of tiger is found in the forests of India, but is now endangered because there are only around 2,500 individuals left in the wild.

1 Tea is a popular drink.

2 Goa has many beaches.

3 Red Fort, Delhi.

4 Cricket is the most popular sport.

Cookery Course

Handfuls of spices go into creating meals of tasty rice, naan bread, curry, popadams, and chutneys. Can you guess which food to add to each table by working out the sequences?

Special Symmetry

Did you know that the left side of the Taj Mahal mirrors the right in real life? Can you spot the five differences between these two pictures of the Taj?

NEPAL

You can stand on top of the planet in Nepal, because it is home to eight of the top ten highest mountains in the world. It is the only country with a non-rectangular flag—the two triangles represent the Himalayan mountains.

KATHMANDU

The capital of the country is rich with history and has seven UNESCO World Heritage sites—three Durbar Squares (historical urban areas), two Buddhist stupas, and two Hindu temples.

BOUDHANATH STUPA

This Buddhist stupa (a dome-shaped shrine) is the largest in the country and a holy site.

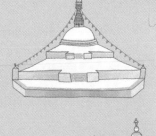

MOUNT EVEREST

The tallest mountain in the world reaches 8,848 m (29,029 ft) high and is also called "Sagarmāthā" and "Chomolungma" by locals.

Kathmandu

3

1

2

THE GOLDEN TEMPLE

This monastery was built in 1409 and two large elephant statues guard the entrance. The metal plates that cover the front of the building make it sparkle, hence the nickname.

SNOW LEOPARD

The beautiful snow leopard lives in the harsh conditions of the snowy mountains. It can leap six times the length of its body.

1 Go whitewater rafting in Bhote Kosi.

2 The Kali Gandaki Gorge, Himalayas.

3 The birthplace of Buddha is at Lumbini.

Buddha's Beliefs

Gautama Buddha was a teacher and Buddhism is the religion based on his beliefs. Buddhist temples always contain an image or statue of Buddha. Can you pick the correct jigsaw piece to finish this picture of Buddha?

A

B

C

D

FINISH

On Top of the World

It is very hard to climb to the top of Everest. Which of these routes is the pathway to the peak?

A B C

CHINA

This country has the world's largest population, and what brings everyone together is the annual festival of the Lunar New Year. Decorative red paper lanterns symbolize the luck, success, and happiness people strive for.

KUNG FU

This is the name for various Chinese martial arts (styles of fighting) that have developed over hundreds of years.

THE GREAT WALL

This epic wall was built to defend China from invasion. It was extended over and over again by different emperors, and reaches around 21,000 km (13,000 miles) in length.

FORBIDDEN CITY

For almost 500 years, this palace in Beijing was home to the emperors of China. Regular people were not allowed inside, hence the name.

Beijing

GIANT PANDAS

These cute black and white bears live only in bamboo forests in China.

1

2

3

1 The Yangtze river.
2 Shanghai Tower.
3 Skyscrapers, Hong Kong.

TERRACOTTA ARMY

Hundreds of life-size soldiers, horses, and chariots were created as an army to guard Emperor Qin Shi Huang's tomb.

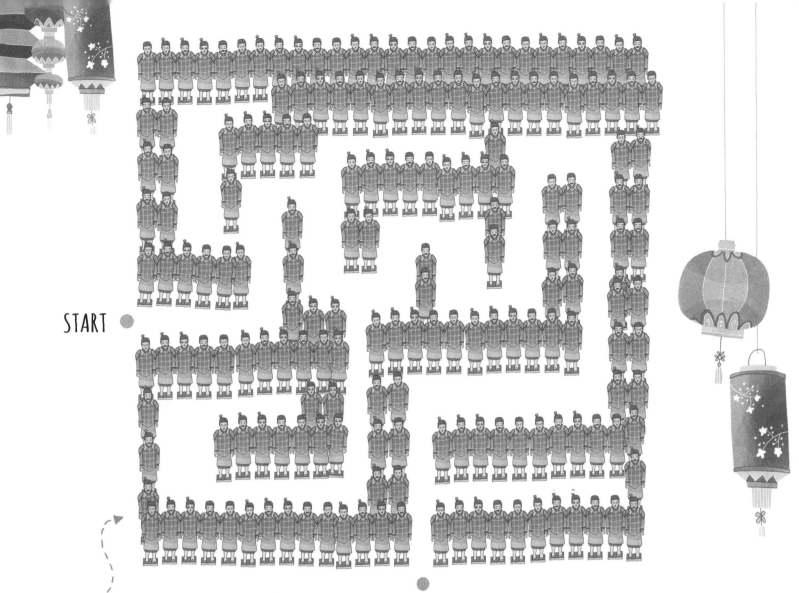

START

FINISH

Maze of Warriors

Can you navigate through this army of terracotta statues?

Panda Pairs

Look at the markings on their fur and see if you can pair up these mother and baby pandas.

A   B   C   D   E   F   G   H

SOUTH KOREA

The native red-crowned crane is a symbol of long life, purity, and peace in South Korea. The country is known for its high-tech cities, but also its tranquil countryside and long history.

2

WINTER OLYMPICS

Pyeongchang was the host of the 2018 Winter Olympic Games.

1

Seoul

HAN RIVER

The Han River runs through the city of Seoul. Hop on a river cruise at night to see the bright lights of the modern skyscrapers on either side of the water.

3

JEJU ISLAND

This relaxing vacation destination for South Koreans is also home to the Hallasan volcano—but don't worry, it hasn't erupted for more than 1,000 years.

ANCIENT PALACE

Gyeongbokgung Palace was built in 1395 and is the largest, and the most famous, of the royal palaces in Seoul.

MUD FESTIVAL

Every year there's a mud festival in Boryeong. Thousands come to this coastal town to play in the mud, and also because the goop is meant to be good for the skin.

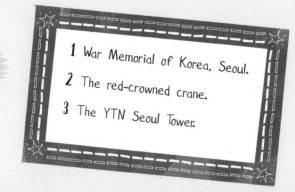

1 War Memorial of Korea, Seoul.

2 The red-crowned crane.

3 The YTN Seoul Tower.

Crane or Ibis?

An ibis has snuck into this herd of cranes. Can you spot it?

? _____

A   B   C

Skating for Gold

Figure skating is a popular sport at the Winter Olympics and these two skaters are going for gold. But which move comes next in their routines? Circle the correct option.

A   B   C   **?** _____

JAPAN

In Japan, delicate cherry blossoms and traditional wooden castles sit side by side with bright neon lights and modern glass skyscrapers. It is this balance of old and new that makes the island nation of Japan so interesting to explore!

1 Sumo wrestling is a national sport.

2 Matsumoto Castle in Nagano Prefecture is a famous historic castle.

3 You can ski in the north...

4 ...and scuba dive in the south.

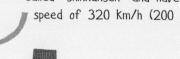

★ Tokyo

BULLET TRAINS

Japan's high-speed trains are called "shinkansen" and have a top speed of 320 km/h (200 mph).

MOUNT FUJI

Japan's tallest peak is 3,776 m (12,388 ft) high. But this peaceful snow—covered mountain is actually a volcano, and last erupted in 1707.

BUSY CITY

Modern Tokyo is famous for its neon-lit skyscrapers and fast pace of life. Try crossing the road in Shibuya at the same time as up to 1,000 other people!

GOLDEN PAVILION

This ancient Buddhist temple in Kyoto is covered in gold. Its shimmering surface is beautifully reflected in the pond in front of it.

TORII SHRINES

Torii gates mark the entrance to a Shinto shrine. One of the most recognized is the gate at Miyajima— it looks as if it is floating on water when the tide comes in.

Single Number Sudoku

Did you know that the puzzle name Sudoku comes from Japan and means "single number?" Can you complete this Sudoku puzzle by making sure there is one of each number in every row, column, and mini-grid?

		3		1	
5	6		3	2	
	5	4	2		3
2		6	4	5	
	1	2		4	5
	4		1		

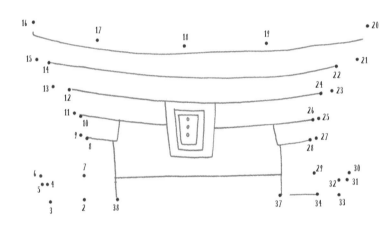

Open the Gate

Torii gates mark the entrance to a Shinto shrine. Because there are no actual gates, the shrine is always open! Join up the dots to complete this gate.

START

FINISH

VIETNAM

Vietnam's charm comes from the influence of many different cultures—just look around to see French colonial buildings sat next to Hội An's Japanese Covered Bridge, and traditional Chinese shops alongside modern corporate offices in Ho Chi Minh City.

HANOI

The capital of Vietnam is famous for the millions of motorcycles whizzing around the city streets. Look out for bikes loaded with people, goods, and even animals!

HẠ LONG BAY

Sail away into this bay of limestone islands topped with trees.

IMPERIAL CITY

This walled palace in Huế was built in the early 1800s and was home to the Nguyễn Dynasty, the last of the powerful families to rule Vietnam.

HỘI AN

Pretty Hội An has a delightful riverside setting and traditional ways of life still blossom here. Many locals often wear the iconic conical "Nón lá" hat, made from palm leaves.

GIÁC LÂM PAGODA

This is one of the oldest Buddhist temples in Ho Chi Minh City, dating from 1744. An impressive shrine with seven levels also sits in the grounds.

Hanoi

1 Reunification Palace, Ho Chi Minh City.

2 Sapa is famous for its rice paddies.

3 The Mekong Delta.

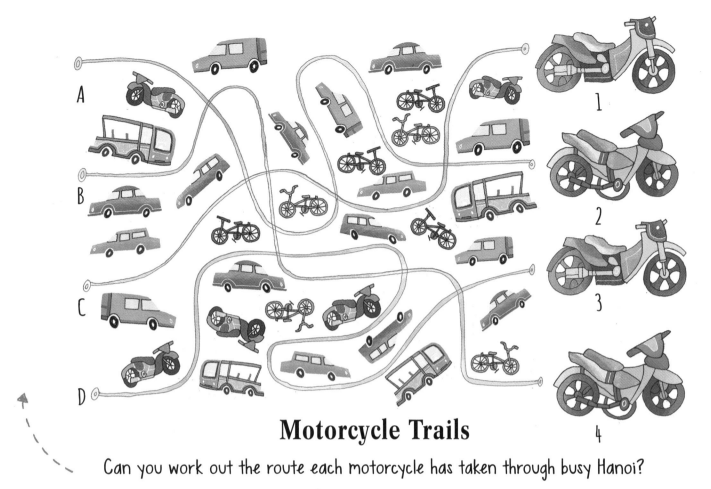

Motorcycle Trails

Can you work out the route each motorcycle has taken through busy Hanoi?

Jigsaw Junk Ship

The traditional junk ships sailing in Hạ Long Bay are wooden boats with sails divided into sections. Can you tell which piece completes this jigsaw?

AUSTRALASIA AND OCEANIA

This continent is made of the huge landmass of Australia plus New Zealand, New Guinea, and the islands in the southern Pacific Ocean. Because the landmass of Australia has been separate from the other continents for millions of years, unique species of animal like the koala and kangaroo can only be found here.

1 AUSTRALIA

2 NEW ZEALAND

AUSTRALIA

The continent of Australia has a huge mix of habitats that are home to many animals you won't see anywhere else in the world. Indigenous Australians have lived here for over 50,000 years, and their art often shows these special Aussie animals.

MARSUPIALS

This group of mammals carry their young in a pouch. Marsupials native to Australia include kangaroos, koalas, wallabies, possums, wombats, bilbies, and Tasmanian devils.

RED ROCK

In the middle of the country there's a huge red sandstone rock named Uluru.

1 Sail south to Tasmania.

2 The lighthouse at Byron Bay is the most easterly point.

3 See the Twelve Apostles on the Great Ocean Road, Victoria.

4 Surfing is a popular pastime in most coastal areas.

5 Parliament House, Canberra.

Canberra

SYDNEY OPERA HOUSE

The city of Sydney held a competition to design a national opera house in 1956. It was won by a Danish architect, Jørn Utzon, with his iconic shape for the building.

CAPITAL CANBERRA

In 1911, when the country couldn't agree if Melbourne or Sydney should be the capital, Australia chose to build a new capital city halfway between the two.

GREAT BARRIER REEF

The world's largest coral reef is visible from space. This living structure is home to countless fish, birds, and reptiles.

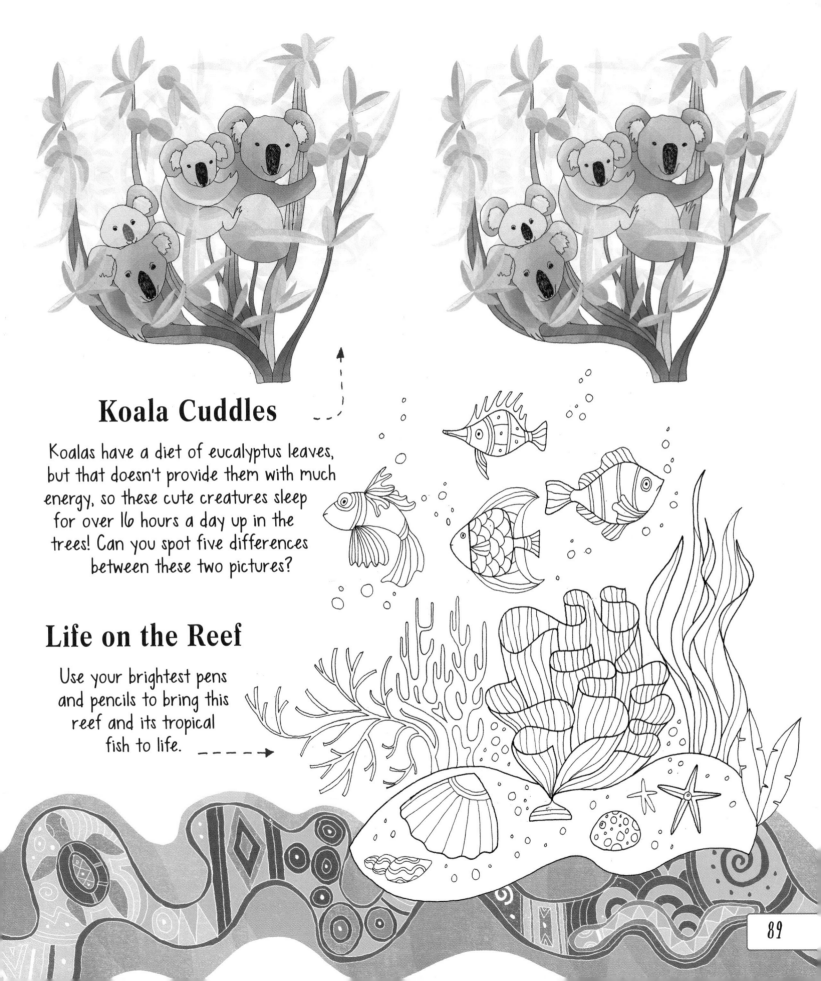

Koala Cuddles

Koalas have a diet of eucalyptus leaves, but that doesn't provide them with much energy, so these cute creatures sleep for over 16 hours a day up in the trees! Can you spot five differences between these two pictures?

Life on the Reef

Use your brightest pens and pencils to bring this reef and its tropical fish to life.

NEW ZEALAND

This country has the wow factor when it comes to scenery, and it's all thanks to the movement of planet Earth's plates under New Zealand's two main islands. Māori culture is a key part of life here and you might even be welcomed with a "pōwhiri" ceremony.

GEOTHERMAL NATION

New Zealand sits on the meeting point of two of Earth's tectonic plates. Heat from inside the planet seeps out through this joint and creates geothermal features such as exploding geysers, bubbling mud pools, and boiling ground water.

GLOWWORM CAVES

Thousands of glowworms live in underground caves at Waitomo. Their glow makes the ceiling of the cave look like the sky at night.

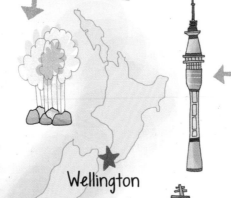

3

Wellington

2

SKY TOWER

Auckland's Sky Tower is the tallest freestanding structure in the southern hemisphere.

THE ALL BLACKS

Rugby Union is the national sport of New Zealand and the both the women's and the men's national teams—both known as the All Blacks—are frequently the best in the world. They perform the haka war dance before each game.

4

1

MILFORD SOUND

In the south of the South Island, this spectacular fjord with its towering mountains was created by a glacier during the Ice Age.

1 Sperm whales visit the east coast.

2 Bungee jumping is popular here.

3 Mount Cook is the highest point in the country.

4 Travel between the North and South islands by ferry.

Nature's Show

Use this map of the geothermal park to navigate from start to finish and avoid the boiling mud, steaming geysers, and scorching pools of water.

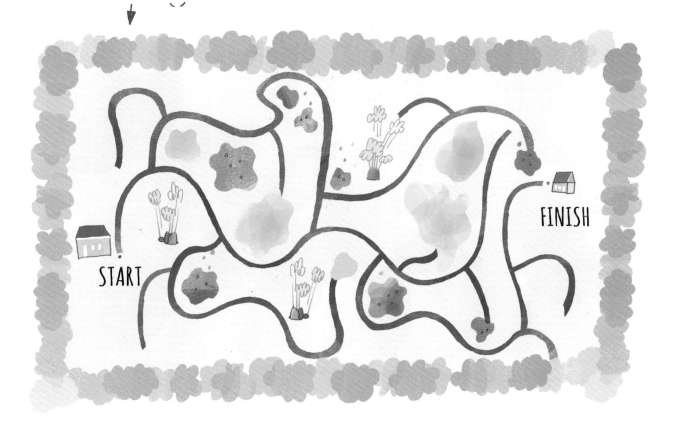

START

FINISH

Pouwhenua Pairs

Can you pair up the Maori symbols carved into this "pouwhenua" totem pole? Which one is the odd one out?

ANTARCTICA

This continent at the southern end of the globe is unlike the others—it has no countries and no permanent population. Extreme temperatures mean most of it is frozen land, and parts of the Southern Ocean surrounding it are also frozen solid. But it does make a good home to seals, penguins, and sea birds.

Antarctica does not have a permanent
human population, only visiting scientists
and tourists, so there is no government.
It does not have an official flag.

Only two penguin species (the Adélie and emperor)
live all year round in Antarctica, but chinstrap,
gentoo, and macaroni penguins breed there.

93

ANSWERS

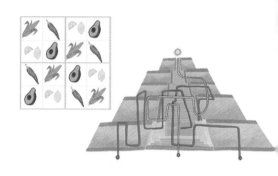

PAGE 9

PAGE 11

PAGE 13

PAGE 23

PAGE 25

PAGE 29

PAGE 31

PAGE 39

PAGE 41

PAGE 43

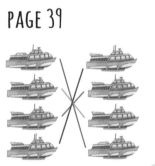

PAGE 55

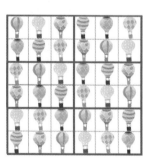

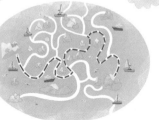

PAGE 53

PAGE 57

PAGE 61

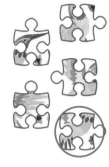

PAGE 15   PAGE 19   PAGE 21

PAGE 33   PAGE 35   PAGE 37

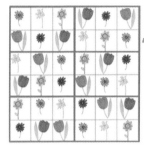

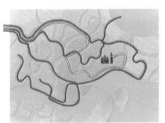

PAGE 49   PAGE 51

PAGE 45   PAGE 47

1 = 7
2 = 3
5 = 8
4 = 6

16 FEET

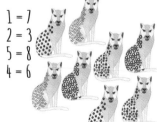

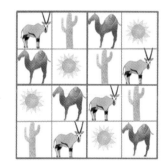

PAGE 63   PAGE 65   PAGE 67   PAGE 71

PAGE 75

PAGE 77

PAGE 73

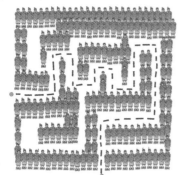

A & D
B & E
C & G
F & H

PAGE 79

C

C

PAGE 81

4	2	3	5	1	6
5	6	1	3	2	4
1	5	4	2	6	3
2	3	6	4	5	1
3	1	2	6	4	5
6	4	5	1	3	2

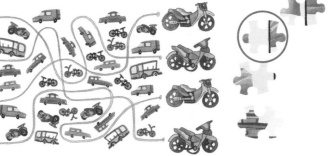

PAGE 83

A = 2   C = 1
B = 4   D = 3

PAGE 85

PAGE 89

PAGE 91